C000126520

GOOD
FOR
A
GRIN

Brenda Burling

First Published 2018 by:
Matthew James Publishing Ltd
Unit 46 Goyt Mill
Upper Hibbert Lane
Marple
SK6 7HX

www.matthewjamespublishing.com

ISBN: 978-1-910265-68-0

© Brenda Burling

The moral rights of the author have been asserted.
Apart from any fair dealing for the purpose of research, or private study, or
criticism or review as permitted under the Copyright, Designs and Patents
Act, 1988, this publication may only be reproduced, stored or transmitted
in any form, or by any means, with the prior permission of the publisher, or
in the case of reprographic reproduction, in accordance with the terms of
licences issued by the Copyright Licensing Agency. Enquiries concerning
reproduction outside those terms should be sent to the publisher.

Printed by Chapel Print Ltd
ROCHESTER | www.chapelprint.com

Illustrations by Angela Chick
www.angelachick.com

FOR ALL THE BOYS.

This book, as with so many, came about almost as a sibling to another. First there was *Might Make You Smile* with its stories, encounters and adventures with so many lovely ladies. *Might Make You Smile* was released and then came the next bunch of writing thoughts. In the forefront of my mind was: 'What about the guys?'

Good For A Grin was born, at least in my mind anyway. It was however a project that was almost shelved, many times. This was only because I had it in my mind that it may in fact not be possible to even create the book. Would anyone want to talk to me? Do guys even want to talk about cancer? Well, as you will see, it turns out that yes indeed, men are as keen to share their experiences with others. Yes, ladies, we may be wrong on this note. Men do like to talk – we just need to ask, but most importantly, listen.

Take it away, fellas!

Brenda

ACKNOWLEDGEMENTS

Writing *Good For A Grin* simply wouldn't have been possible without the help of so very many people. I would firstly like to thank each and every contributor for sharing their lives and stories with me. I can say without exception that every person I have communicated with on any level has been nothing but enthusiastic in wanting to get the word out there and share their experience, in the hope that it helps even just one person. You are all utterly amazing people and I am deeply honoured to have had the privilege to share your experiences.

I would like to personally thank all the organisations I have come across who have given their time to see me, talk with me and share with me. These include OddBalls Foundation, Battling Fat Lads, Maggie's Cancer Centres and Life Kitchen. It is great to know there are organisations, groups and places where people are made to feel at home, and offered comfort and support. I am delighted to be associated with so many organisations that raise awareness, provide support and remove the isolation for all those affected by cancer.

CONTENTS

FOREWORD

RYAN RILEY
FOUNDER OF LIFE KITCHEN

When I founded *Life Kitchen* the main focus was to bring a touch of joy in a time of darkness. Cancer can be very dark, I'd been touched by it five times before I was twenty years old. The hardest experience was watching my own mother, Krista go through it. She struggled, I struggled, but what came out of the darkness was a world of love, light and appreciation.

The simple times in which we ate together are my most treasured. Whether it was a sit down table meal or eating on the sofa on a tray, it brought us together. Food was a problem for my mother, the chemotherapy robbed her taste and that has always stuck with me.

I knew my mother's taste had really gone when we sat down for a meal in Spain after her wedding vow renewal and she bit into what she thought was an apple from the table centrepiece. It turned out to be an onion. Two bites went by without her noticing until I turned to her and pointed out that it wasn't an apple. That story for me is tinged with sadness, but we all broke out into hysterical laughter because out of all tragedy and pain there is a deep thing inside of us that helps find the laughter and light in any situation. This was a moment in time for me.

Taste, the founding principal of *Life Kitchen,* and I guess of most things in life, is so important to not only our enjoyment of food but our mental health, our social lives and our time spent with loved ones.

Life kitchen runs free cookery classes focused on taste and flavour for people living with cancer right across the UK and although my mother is no longer here she lives on in these recipes and in Life Kitchen.

FOLLOW US ON TWITTER:
@LIFEKITCHEN @RYANRILEYY

HOW THE TIE IN WITH OddBalls CAME ABOUT

So, with the idea for the new book in mind, there then came a need for a charity. *Might Make You Smile* had Helen Rollason Cancer Charity, now *Good For A Grin* needed one too.

For some reason the search for a male cancer charity was a little harder. I talked to lots of different people and found out that so many of the charities had their own policies on being associated or involved with outside projects. Some even had a 'donation first' policy, which sometimes ran into thousands of pounds. My own thoughts on this were that it was somewhat discouraging to anyone wanting to help/benefit a charity. I suppose, however, that a charity is in fact still a business, and businesses need protecting.

Anyway, their loss is our gain; there were a couple of suggestions and it was from these that I came across OddBalls. Read up on them, their ethos, their underwear, you name it. It looked perfect. Being a rugby fan myself only added to the attraction as there appeared to be a huge involvement with the whole rugby world, as well as many other sporting and entertainment endeavours. Now it was just the reach-out to be done. I am a person who needs a run-up at most things in life, and yes, contacting charities and companies sits slap bang in the middle of this state.

As it turned out, the phone call to Will and Julian was perhaps the easiest I have ever made on this sort of matter. Firstly, yes, it was actually them I spoke to (I kid you not), not a person acting on behalf of another person who once was the second cousin of the MD etc, etc. No, seriously, it was and still is one of the easiest organisations I have had the pleasure to deal with.

The response was: "Yes, they were 'psyched' to be involved,' even after my very long-winded explanation (being a writer, why use three words when thirty-three will suffice?). I truly couldn't believe it was that easy. Going to bed thinking about the way the book was already evolving had me overthinking. By the time the morning came I'd convinced myself that I had perhaps not told them enough, given them the wrong impression, misinformed them, even misunderstood them and they were in fact not interested, you name it.

A few days later I was begging my publishers to get in contact and really go through with them the concept of *Good For A Grin*. I waited. The publishers came back saying yes! It really was true, OddBalls was on board and excited. A few more days passed, a shout out was compiled and agreed on, and within days the announcement was out. Brenda Burling, Matthew James Publishing and the great OddBalls were working together. Time to stop pinching myself and get writing.

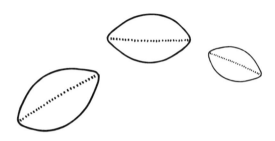

RUGBY SAVED MY LIFE...
Or so my mate says

Dan was a rugby man, which made his wife a rugby 'widow'. Unlike a football widow, she would wait for her beloved to come home to regale her with a blow-by-blow account (yes, in rugby terms this is a literal thing – black eyes and a variety of injuries always accompany the account and are always sported with a large degree of pride). Dan, however, was a rugby man with a sore testicle. The testicle in question had been giving him some grief. Dan was convinced it was just another of those 'rugby' injuries. Just how much it affected him, however, was brought home during a full 'hands on' incident in the middle of a match, which left him in absolute agony, having never felt such excruciating pain before.

As anyone who has the vaguest understanding of rugby will know, injuries are like trophies to all, bar the wives and girlfriends of rugby players. Getting your nuts bashed, along with every other part of your body, is nothing new. This is rugby after all, there's no crying over a broken nail here.

It was only when Dan (at the behest of his wife – yes, they really do know best) had a swollen gland in his neck checked out that he bit the bullet, manned up and said: "While I'm here, Doc, would you mind checking my testicles. I'm not sure everything is right." Dan was given the diagnosis he dreaded most, it was suspected he had testicular cancer. A referral to a consultant was agreed.

For a number of reasons, Dan decided to blog his experiences from the moment he was diagnosed. One, he could share his experiences with anyone else who might find themselves in the same situation, thereby giving himself the opportunity to look back and recollect how far he had come; and secondly, so his wife Nat didn't have to keep relaying the same information to people over and over again. He also wanted to document both the treatments and the wonderful care he received during his experience.

In his blog he says: "Also, very importantly, I've read blogs that related to my issues and I found them useful for what I was about to go through – if this helps one person through the process and makes others aware, then the effort to write it all down will be worth it."

Dan was prepared to share everything. His main mantras throughout were always positive: "It will all be fine," "Everything will be o.k." and "No matter the odds, never give up." The third one was said to him by a colleague, Craig, who lost his battle, but his words went on to become a part of Dan's family's mantra.

Dan's team mates all vouched for him, claiming that Nat had no future recourse on the rugby front from now on, as it was indeed thanks to the great game of rugby that Dan's life had been saved.

MAN'S
NATURAL POSE

Yes, Gareth was relaxed, slouched back on the sofa, hand down his pants cupping his nuts, watching T.V. in man's most natural pose. Mmm… something wasn't quite right down there. One was definitely larger than the other and not in the usual way, there was distinctive swelling. Something was up.

The next day Gareth sensibly took himself of to the docs. His wife's pleading was ringing in his ear: "Can you just tell them you found a lump, rather than sounding like some weird pervert?" Gareth, however, was all for authenticity: if he was lounging with his hand down his pants when making his discovery, so be it. Tell it as it is.

The doctor diagnosed an infection and made a non-urgent referral for four to six weeks.

Unsatisfied, but in the usual, true, polite British manner, Gareth said "Thank you very much" and left.

As is often the case at these sort of times, Gareth quickly came to his senses and marched straight back into the surgery. A little shouting, and possibly accompanied by some gesticulating (we all know the details become vague when the red mist falls) later he was granted an urgent referral. Probably given partly in the hope of getting him to leave the premises quicker, but he had the urgent referral nonetheless.

His diagnosis for testicular cancer was confirmed and bollock removal (orchidectomy) surgery was scheduled.

By the time the day for the surgery arrived, Gareth and his wife had welcomed their new baby, Finley, and been immersed in the craziness and the full sleep-deprived existence of parenting for two weeks – they were exhausted. At the hospital, Gareth was on his bed in the pre-operative waiting area – his wife saw her opportunity for much needed sleep, (new baby remember) and climbed onto the bed and under the covers. In no time the couple drifted off into a deep sleep.

They were woken by the surgeon, who frankly couldn't get over how "relaxed" Gareth was about the procedure. Parent of a beautiful baby boy, wife snuggled up beside him – losing a nut was hardly going to put too much of a dampener on things.

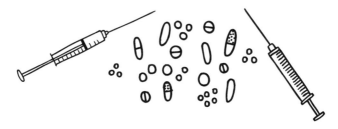

LIFE IS A ROLLERCOASTER

Mike had his suspicions. Trips to the bathroom throughout the night, nothing new there, but when instead of pee he noticed there was blood, the voice inside his head told him it was time to get things checked out.

He did just that. Unfortunately the timing of the discovery was not the greatest. Mike and his wife Ann were in the process of challenging a district council 120 miles away from where they lived concerning council tax on their apartment on the coast. They had an appointment to meet a council representative and really didn't want to miss it, but the health issue was acute.

The decision between Mike and his wife was to make an appointment with their G.P. and take it from there. At the appointment that morning, the G.P. asked Mike what he thought the problem was. He explained his thoughts were that it was either something or nothing. Mike had, however, been concerned with the threat of cancer – it had been at the back of his mind for the past ten years or so, having had so many relatives die from the disease. The G.P. was very understanding, neither alarmist nor understating the possible situation.

Various blood tests were booked. The conveyor belt had started. After the tests, there were appointments at Addenbrooke's within the following two weeks. Mike's anxieties rose during this time. The obvious questions, 'Have I got cancer?', 'Yes' and 'No' were bouncing around his head, the stakes rising higher and higher.

Kidneys and bladder were scanned, cystoscopy performed, and, lastly prostate palpitated. Mike felt something during the palpitation. The consultant explained things looked clear but that there was a nodule; it could just have been harmless but he would take the results to the Multi-Disciplinary Team and get back to him with the outcome.

Mike and his wife shared their concerns. Ann's first husband had died of cancer at seventy, so here she was again with a similar possibility. She and Mike were able to support each other as the conveyor belt of tests, scans and appointments continued. Life, as is always the case, still carried on. Dealing with other issues was both a distraction and sometimes an inconvenience.

Trying to focus and concentrate on daily activities was difficult. Ann and Mike decided they would tell their families as an M.R.I. scan appointment was getting closer and they would need help from their children taking care of things, including Ann's mum, who was in a care home.

Mike received a 'Summary of Pending Results and Final Plan, in the post. He read cytology benign (normal) and was ecstatic, he was free from cancer. He quickly sent an email to all friends and family and even his G.P. to that effect. He was on a high, life could get back to being normal. He had had a scare but all was well.

Two days later Mike got a telephone call. It was the cancer nurse specialist (obviously to confirm the good news). What he actually heard was that he had a grade five growth. A grade five growth was highly suspicious. Mike explained he had received the report stating 'cytology benign (normal)'. "Ahh, you're reading the urine sample results," she said. The nurse went on to explain there was in fact the possibility he did have cancer.

The anxieties rose to new heights. The conveyor belt was about to pick up pace again. He felt so alone, cold, and remembered an advert he had seen on the television for Macmillan nurses – the man was alone in a hospital gown in a barren landscape. He could completely relate to it.

Bizarrely, it was at that point that his humour came to the fore. He caught himself saying to nobody in particular: "There's no need to go to Alton Towers, I'm getting a rollercoaster ride for nothing, it's all on the NHS!" Up and down, round and round, up and down again, the emotions never seemed to stop. He had to smile to himself, his sense of humour was still intact, if slightly warped. Hardly surprising, but still there nonetheless.

FOR THE LOVE
OF RUGBY

Ben could hear the pounding of booted feet behind him. He was so close to the touchline he could almost taste it.

His heart was racing, the try was his. He just had to reach out as his arm extended and put the ball firmly in place. Control of the movement was all-important, all he could think of was "Don't drop the ball, don't drop the ball."

The pain was the first thing he registered, a searing, burning, take your breath away pain that was so severe it rendered him speechless. Perhaps a better description would be soundless. He wanted to scream, yell, whatever, but the shock of the severity of the pain seemed to have rendered him incapable.

"Sorry mate, you ok?" The opposition team member was looking down at Ben. Ben was still incapable of moving. His hands had naturally gone to his testicles, where the damage had been done. He waited for the pain to subside and catch his breath.

Eventually he was able to get up, though the pain was still an eleven on the one-to-ten scale. The try had been awarded. Ben was delighted, if not incredibly sore. Limping off the pitch, he couldn't believe the pain was still so strong. The beers that followed the game helped a little, however.

The following morning, Ben was still very sore and hugely swollen. He told himself it was all due to the smack 'down there' he had been on the receiving end of during the match. But he was aware the swelling didn't look like it was going down. Thinking it best to get it checked out, he went to hospital, still putting everything down to the rugby accident. Scans were ordered and completed. There was a little niggle at the back of his mind that was kept there by the old "It will never happen to me" adage.

After numerous scans and appointments Ben got the news he had dreaded, he had testicular cancer. The issue was with Ben's right testicle and it needed to be removed. The date for the operation was made.

Ben arrived at the hospital and waited to meet the surgeon. She came into the consulting room. "So, let's have a look at this LEFT testicle that's been giving you all these problems," she said as she knelt down in front of Ben. "Actually, the problem is with the right testicle," Ben replied. He quickly dropped his shorts. The surgeon took his testicles in her hands for examination. "Oh, yes!" she said. "You are quite right. That's lucky, we could have taken the wrong one!"

Ben wasn't quite sure how he felt about her remark. He was, however, very relieved when he came round from the operation, lifted the bed sheet and discovered the right one had gone and the left one was left.

⊖ ⊖ ⊖ ⊖ ⊖ ⊖ ⊖ ⊖

PREGGERS?...

On October 24th, James was diagnosed with testicular cancer. He had noticed a lump and had taken himself off to the doctors, to be told it was nothing to worry about.

Two more weeks passed and James realised the lump wasn't getting any smaller. He was pondering his predicament when he recalled reading a story a few years previously about a guy who had, as a joke, taken a pregnancy test and it showed up positive. Being somewhat gobsmacked, the man had looked into the result further, it being not exactly expected, and it transpired he had cancer! James decided he would do the same thing. He got exactly the same result. James ,according to the 'stick', was pregnant!

The next day James went to the doctor, who got him to take another test. The same thing happened. James was definitely pregnant! The reason for this phenomenon is that when women are pregnant they produce a hormone that can also be found in some testicular cancers.

Within a day, James was at the hospital to have the findings confirmed. He did in fact have cancer.

The following week, James was admitted to have the operation to remove his right testicle (orchidectomy). A painful couple of weeks recovering followed. The operation was a success, and after a time James was able to return to work.

As is often the case there will be future scans and appointments, all helping to keep an eye on things. From the strangest of findings James was diagnosed and treated. He was very impressed with the level of care he received and deeply grateful to all the doctors and nurses involved. It is their care we rely on, after all.

So, fellas, should you be inclined and choose to pee on that stick, rest assured you won't be the first.

OH WHAT A NIGHT!

Nick's discovery of his testicular cancer came about in a somewhat unorthodox way. A thirty-one-year-old single dad, working as a police officer, juggling life and after a very successful night out with a lovely lady (no beer goggle disaster there) discovers he is a little 'tender' the following morning. Upon closer inspection he noticed a small lump on his left testicle and it was a little painful to touch.

While getting the results from having a growth removed from his neck, Nick had mentioned the lump on his testicle, pants down. A few more questions were asked about Nick's medical history, and when he mentioned he had had an operation to descend a testicle when he was ten, the doctor straight away sent him for an ultrasound scan. Pants up.

Pants down again, Nick asked the radiographer if she could tell him what was going on. He explained he didn't mean to be awkward or was going to get angry, he just would really like to know what was happening.. She was a lovely lady and showed him the scan. It was obvious there was something on the left testicle that didn't look right. Pants up and back to the doctor again. Dropping his pants once more, Nick realised it was becoming second nature by now; interesting habit to have, he mused.

At the doctors, he was told he would receive the full results the following week. It was a few days later that Nick was asked to St. James Hospital, Leeds. At the hospital, the discussion of further children in the future came up and it was recommended that a sperm sample be deposited. Nick considered this a fair point. Finding the department where this was to be done, he walked into a very large and busy main waiting area.

There were a number of other people there for various other appointments. It was obvious they were certainly not all there for the same reason as Nick. His name was called, and he was somewhat ceremoniously handed a cup and shown to a room. Pants down again. When the deposit had been made, was Nick able to leave discreetly by a separate exit with his dignity intact? Did a nurse quietly knock on the door and remove the sample for him? Unfortunately not – Nick had to take his sample, cup in hand, straight back to the main reception and hand it over in front of a waiting room full of people. Yes, it was obvious to all exactly what he had been up to.

There was no other cause of action to take, other than to smile sweetly and walk with definite purpose out of the waiting room.

MIKE'S MAD DASH

Mike had discovered a lump on his testicle. He knew he had to be proactive and get it checked out as soon as possible. He was a father of one and expecting his second child any day now. His family was everything to him. It would have been the easiest thing to wait until the new arrival was there and then get things looked into, but he was also aware that these things needed to be acted on quickly – time was of the essence.

Admittedly, with his wife heavily pregnant the timing could have been better, but that is just the way life is. Within two weeks his operation was scheduled, Mike had testicular cancer and his testicle needed to be removed.

Life threw him another curve ball as he was having his operation at Pinderfields Hospital – his wife went into labour at Dewsbury and District Hospital in Wakefield.

As soon as Mike came round from his operation he was off making his uncomfortable way to Dewsbury to be with his wife. He arrived to see his daughter being born, and thanks to his quick actions and resulting early detection, he is now enjoying watching his two daughters grow up.

Mike is a member of Battling Fat Lads football team. They are sponsored by the OddBalls Foundation and raise money through charity football matches. They are also regular competitors in the FA People's Cup.

BOWEL MOVEMENTS AND PEEING

So, as with so many medical events, when diagnosing and being diagnosed with cancer, whatever type of cancer it is, the age-old questions come into play.

"Do you poo regularly?", "How often do you poo?", "Have you noticed any changes in your poo?"

Same goes for peeing. "Do you find you have the urge to pee more?", "What colour is your pee?", "How much, roughly, do you think you pee?"

Now, from a male point of view, peeing, farting and pooing are all perfect fodder for comedy and regaling, bringing forth a great deal of merriment; but when it comes down to taking much more serious notice of these things, no, it is not always top of our agenda.

Did we have a skinfull Saturday night after the England rugby match? Yes, yes we did. Did I pee a lot? Of course. Was it closely followed by a much anticipated chicken vindaloo, Bombay potatoes and hot pickle-eating contest? Yes, yes it was. Did I poo a lot? You betcha!

You can see how hard it can be for the average male to even contemplate a change in either of these habits. We barely take notice of them normally.

It usually takes something dramatic to make us notice something. Only when this 'notice' has been taken do things move forward.

So my advice would be; after reading this, for a couple of days just take a little more notice of what your body does.

Yes, stare at that poo (no, it is not necessary to poke it with a stick, leave that to the medical profession, should they choose), notice how often you pee. Pay a bit more attention to your body. It might just help you notice something you may have missed.

P.E.T. SCAN MEETS RADIOACTIVE MAN

Blue? Seriously, blue pee? When you have already been told you need to stay clear of pregnant women and children (Not 'pregnant children', in case you were wondering) after having a P.E.T. scan. Blue pee, to boot, had to be seen to be believed. Dave had to smile though as he watched the blue liquid circle the toilet bowl.

Did he feel like a five-year-old boy again, able to glean some amusement and fascination from unusual toilet habits? Yes, yes he did. Did he wish he could share the moment with half a dozen of his mates, who he knew would be equally fascinated and fully appreciate the spectacle? Yes, yes he did.

The knock at the door and the nurse's voice asking if he was okay brought him back from his reverie. "Are you okay in there Dave?"

"Fine, thanks nurse." He didn't think the nurse would be as fascinated as he was with his colourful accomplishments. . Having been told to flush twice, to make sure all radioactive residue was dispelled, Dave made his way back to the cubicle.

He had been given a list of precautionary things he needed to know about after his scan. Dave felt a little bit like a pioneer, having to break new ground in science with his radioactivity and azure emissions. In truth, he knew many had gone before him, doing exactly the same thing, but he enjoyed the moment for what it was. Peeing on command (as was required after the actual scan) had never been an issue for Dave and he was somewhat pleased with himself that he could empty his bladder as and when commanded. This was accompanied by much praise from the radiographer.

The precautions varied from keeping bodily fluids away from others, changing bed sheets if necessary and the need for glove-wearing nursing staff. Dave allowed his imagination to take over, visions of himself in steel worker mode, wearing elbow-length industrial gloves, a rubber smock apron, and full-face welding mask, popped into his head, looking somewhat similar to the executioner from one of the *Black Adder* series. In reality, light disposable gloves were worn by the nurses with nothing for him (he was, after all, the 'radioactive' one).

Having read something somewhere that a P.E.T. scan might set off radiation alarms at airports, Dave discovered he had almost an all-consuming urge to test this theory at the nearest one. Fortunately, the nearest was hours away.

Dave, when he was back in the comfort of his chair, beside his bed, scan completed and enjoying a cup of tea, came to the con-clusion that being diagnosed with cancer had, among other things, made him more creative in his thinking and had reignited a somewhat neglected mischievous side to his nature. He felt this needed to be both embraced and exploited. Yes, it could be time to have a little fun, he mused. Look out, world.

PUMP NO.1 AND PUMP NO.2

Fred was having a hard time dealing with the after-effects of his prostatectomy. For many men the two main problems are incontinence and E.D., the abbreviation for erectile dysfunction.

Fred had been made very aware of these issues prior to his surgery, but reading information leaflets, articles online and anything he could get his hands on was all very well – living with these issues day-to-day was a whole different matter. Fred was a man who possessed a great sense of humour and was always one to give advice along the lines of 'get it done, get it sorted, move on with life', always accompanied with a huge smile and a slap on the back. He found he was now having difficulty taking his own advice.

43

The euphoria – yes, that's right, euphoria – of having his surgery and knowing the biggest part of his encounter with prostate cancer had now been removed (a large tumour attached to the prostate), had now worn off. He had also been warned again that this was often the case. Alas, a warning is just that, a warning. Fred realised fairly quickly he needed help. He knew if he could get assistance with the physical side of his rehabilitation, then his emotional and mental wellbeing would follow suit. Coming to terms with this realisation made him ponder if this was in fact the 'male way' of dealing with things. If he were able to cope and ultimately flourish with the physical side of life, he felt maybe a man's mental wellbeing could be all the easier to bring into line.

The incontinence was a particular issue and Fred wanted it sorted. At meetings with his consultant and medical team, an artificial sphincter was discussed, the procedure involving a sphincter being placed around the urethra, with the central pump placed in the scrotum. To aid with erectile disfunction, and at around the same time, it was suggested that a cylinder be placed in the penis, a reservoir inserted into the abdomen and a pump placed in the scrotum.

Fred thought about all this information very carefully. In the midst of this he burst out laughing, perhaps not the best time, being in the consulting room, but he had to explain. It really wouldn't do to get the two pumps mixed up.

Ultimately, Fred chose neither option. A regiment of patience and his own brand of 'self-training', learning to predict his body's needs, establishing good routines and perseverance, helped him in the end.

SUCK IT IN, TENSE IT UP, WINDMILL IT IN

Examinations for anything medical can and always will be daunting, even nerve-wracking. However, when it comes to your 'bits' it's a whole new level. Just when you want to at least give a good show of yourself, everything shrinks away and often refuses to co-operate.

On one particular occasion Gareth found himself wearing only his socks, a truly sexy look for anyone, it's got to be said, very *The Graduate*. Wanting to make the most of his 'assets', he was putting himself through some lunges and stretches in his allotted examination room. The stretches were then accompanied by some vigorous 'windmilling' to make his somewhat shrivelled penis look bigger before 'presenting' to the consultant. Yes, this morning he was really putting himself through his paces.

If preparing for an intimate examination of 'the old fella' was an Olympic sport, on this day Gareth could well have qualified for Team GB.

The gods, however, were not smiling down on him on this particular day. He found himself doing the very thing he had laughed at men doing on beaches when an attractive girl sauntered by. Guilty as charged, Gareth was putting in a mammoth effort, holding in his stomach and tensing every single muscle while the very attractive, Italian, female consultant carefully examined him. Let's just say 'awkward!'

AND OLYMPIC GOLD FOR BLADDER MANAGEMENT GOES TO...

If you are not thinking about your bum when being treated for rectal cancer, the likelihood is that you are thinking about your bladder. This was particularly the case for Pat. Having been told the tumour in his rectum needed radio-therapy to reduce it in size (although it would get larger initially, purely because it wouldn't like being zapped) before it could be removed surgically. However, it was important that the radiotherapy was directed very precisely, not only for maximum effectiveness, but also to make sure no other organs were affected.

In Pat's case, the bladder was the organ most likely to be affected if the radiotherapy 'zapping' wasn't exactly right. To control this eventuality, he had to gauge how full his bladder was at every session. The treatment was given in an oval, so getting the contour the same all the way around was paramount. If the bladder were too full, the stomach would be pushed out, making the contour around the middle bigger than at the back. Also, the bladder would be too close to the tumour, and this could then have further implications, including possible bladder problems after the treatment, something Pat definitely wanted to avoid.

Not being full enough didn't help with the procedure either, making it less effective, so guessing fluid intake became an obsession during the radiotherapy treatment. It was all about precision, precision, precision. Too empty meant having to drink a little water, wait ten minutes, get scanned then hopefully have the treatment. Too full was even trickier. Pat had to try to wee a little bit, have another scan and then try for the treatment again.

As everyone who has ever had to do it, weeing just a tiny little bit with a full bladder takes genius-level style concentration (an instant admission to Mensa should be awarded) and precision skill. Both these attributes had to be mastered. In time Pat became proficient to varying degrees, but the days when he didn't have the treatments were a joy, not to be consumed by the drinking…weeing…waiting …drinking…weeing…waiting cycle. These times actually felt like a holiday – not your palm tree-laced, secluded beach, exotic cocktails and balmy temperatures type of holiday, but a holiday nonetheless.

There were however the golden days. Not many, but some regardless, whereby the science – the 'Pat Science' – worked out perfectly and he got it right first time. These were the days when he walked in and bing! The scan showed he had got it absolutely right first time and the treatment went ahead. The challenge came after Pat had managed to attain the perfect score of two for two. Two sessions of radiotherapy had been given without any bladder adjustments. No extra drinking or weeing or waiting. A high five from the radiographer and much back slapping all round, Pat felt like a champion.

The challenge was on! Could he make it three for three?

The day dawned bright and breezy. The athlete went through his routine in his head. Drink a little, wait, wee a little... and repeat.. Arriving at the treatment centre he felt good, but then his instincts kicked in – was he a little full? Was his mind playing tricks on him? It was scan time...the tension was building…the crowd (Pat, radiographer and an assistant) fell into a hushed silence. The scan completed… the wait seemed endless…and then bing! The treatment could go ahead. Pat felt like he had won Gold. In his mind he was making the walk to the podium, stepping up to first position, accepting the medal and bouquet of flowers. Yes, Pat takes Olympic Gold in the great sport of bladder management.

After the treatment there was much celebrating and jubilation, a great day for all.

It's the little things.

AVIARIES OR SHEEP?

Richard and Lorraine had set out on the leaflet drop, up and down pathways and driveways throughout the village. Neither of them minded the walking involved – the fresh air, along with being outdoors and together, was an enjoyable time. In fact, Richard loved pretty much anything active or sports-orientated. If he wasn't walking, cycling, playing cricket, tennis or rugby, to name but a few of his sporting endeavours, then there was definitely something up. Either that or he was taking part in the local Dwyle Flunking competition (a game of two teams, twelve men on each, taking turns to dance around while being slapped by the other team with a beer-soaked cloth, the 'Dwyle'. The result is always contested, and vast amounts of beer consumed.)

It was this aspect of his life that made the recurring gout episodes so very annoying and supremely frustrating. Every now and then he would experience an aggressive flare-up that rendered him immobile. Not a situation someone like Richard appreciated, one little bit. Nor for that matter did Lorraine – a man like Richard was not happy being confined.

It didn't seem to matter what the doctors gave him, even 'horse strength' antibiotics made no difference. So much so that matters were getting worse. Richard became completely confined to the house and then ultimately bedbound, unable to get around at all. It was only when he finally had a blood test performed that acute myeloid leukaemia, not gout, was diagnosed – and it was advanced.

Richard was offered the choice of two clinical trials at Addenbrooke's Hospital in Cambridge, not too far from where they lived. One trial was low risk, though with fewer possible benefits, while the other was much higher risk but with the possibility of far greater rewards, should it work. Lorraine and Richard were expecting a new grandchild around this time, and their family was everything to them both.

Richard was a man who had always aimed high and had strong principles that he lived by, sometimes with interesting outcomes. Occasionally, it had to be said, living by his principles could cause a certain degree of chaos. His past antics included the time he and the late activist John Bugg drove a tank to central London out of protest (for which he was arrested), not to mention the time he cut the wire at RAF Molesworth (for which he was also arrested!). Yes, it was fair to say Richard had always been a risk taker, but he was a man who believed in doing something if you felt strongly enough about it. There was no doubt the high-risk trial was for him, and there was no hesitation whatsoever in his decision.

One thing, however, that had Richard and Lorraine perplexed in the midst of this new information, future prospects, enormous decisions to be made and the knowledge of the likelihood for Richards survival, was when they were asked the question: "Has Richard been around aviaries or sheep?" Stunned, the couple were thrown into a state of bewilderment. Neither could recall anything of the kind. No, they had no plans to open a petting zoo of any description. They hadn't even visited any zoos or farms, although they did live in the countryside, in a village. In the blur of all that had gone on, neither thought to ask why? What significance could this possibly have?

During the darkest times it was this question that made them smile – a bewildered, questioning and perplexing smile, but a smile nonetheless. They never did find out the relevance, but did enjoy pondering the question.

THE COLOURS OF THE RAINBOW

It is amazing the effect that the various drugs used in the treatment and diagnosis of cancer have on everyday bodily functions. There is one in particular that is readily affected and easily measured, and that is urinating.

Who knew that even a scan can produce some interesting effects. You may find that as soon as you go to the toilet after a P.E.T. scan you could be weeing a blue colour. Somewhat disconcerting, yes. A little fascinating, certainly.

Couple this with the patient who is taking a good dose of multi-vitamin (if you are having difficulty eating, often a side effect of chemotherapy and radiotherapy, this may be suggested), which are likely to turn your wee fluorescent yellow or green. A hue that Sigourney Weaver in any scene from *Alien* would be not be surprised at encountering.

Doxorubicin, given in chemotherapy, will, apart from doing exactly what it is supposed to, will often turn your wee a delightful crimson colour. Obviously this can be pretty scary if you haven't been warned and are possibly a little sensitive about what is happening to you anyway. This has been likened to peeing Ribena, and while it's most definitely somewhat more toxic and not to be considered as thirst quenching, it's an interesting analogy nonetheless.

All these things can make for an interesting experience should you find yourself in communal urinals. Still, it could prove to be a fascinating topic of conversation, depending on your audience.

AND THE VOTES ARE IN

With the diagnosis of prostate cancer in, there was now the issue of treatment options for Michael. He and his wife were a team, and a good team at that. Michael was given the choices of radiotherapy or radical prostatectomy. In Mike's mind the words curable and cancer did not go together, but that was exactly what he had – 'curable cancer'. When Michael had questions, fears and concerns it was his wife's calming, stabilising response that kept him going. "We will just have to see, we should get more information when we next see the consultant," she would say, holding her hand out towards him, should he wish to take it in his.

It wasn't a case of dismissing the concern but, stabilising the situation with calm logic, and Ann's own way of showing her support. Mike and Ann decided they would take all the information on both procedures and each would read one lot one evening (not your usual bedtime reading, it had to be said) and then the next evening they would swap. They would leave it twenty-four hours and then there would be a secret ballot when they were both absolutely sure of what both procedures entailed.

It was after they had collected all the information on both procedures that a place called 'Maggie's Wallace', or Maggie's' as it was commonly known, was suggested as a great place to get support, meet others in the same position and where counsellors were available to discuss any aspect of cancer with you. It was to prove invaluable, a comfortable place, full of warmth, information and understanding. As well as tea, coffee, cake and fruit, it was ran by qualified staff and a wonderful collection of volunteers. It was there that Michael and Ann discovered a six-session course on radical prostatectomy. There were also sessions covering diet, relaxation, yoga and tai chi.

Over the two nights Michael and Ann read the reams of information. Michael even created a spreadsheet as he realised there were so many points to consider. As he added up all pros and cons he deduced his choice would be prostatectomy.

The votes were placed. Mike unfolded both pieces of paper. They had each voted for Prostatectomy. They laughed – democracy at its best.

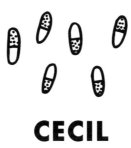

CECIL

Rectal cancer had meant life-saving surgery, and further treatment in the form of chemotherapy and radiotherapy was going to feature heavily in Patrick's life.

First things first, surgery was required. Pat was going to have to join the ranks of the 'ostomates society' (no secret handshakes here just the addition of a little extra luggage). He would need to have a colostomy bag, and for this to happen he was going to require surgery to create a stoma. Obviously, this surgery is life altering in itself, both physically and psychologically. As Pat says, he still poos, just differently. He was quick to realise the need to try to remove the stigma associated with poo and bums, particularly among men, who often don't always talk about things, especially these types of private matters.

To help with this, Patrick started a blog on day one of his actual diagnosis. He wanted to offer as much down-to-earth support, facts and openness to anybody who chose to listen (or in this case, read). He was honest and upfront from the start that there would indeed be toilet talk on all levels, be it poo, bums or farts. Pat wanted it all to be out there in the open. Embarrassment or shying away was not an option.

When the day came for the operation, Patrick had researched as much as possible about his surgery and it was suggested the stoma be named, something to do with helping get around the life-changing event mentally.

On September 14th 2016 Cecil was welcomed into the Reeve household. Pat had no idea why he chose the name Cecil, but it seemed to appeal and stuck immediately. Overnight Cecil became an internet star, featuring heavily in the blog and, as with any newborn, life predominantly now evolved around him.

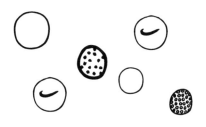

ONE TESTICLE OR TWO?...

"Your friends will always be there with you through thick and thin"

Dan had the diagnosis confirmed to him, he had testicular cancer.

Telling everyone was the hardest bit, once he and his wife Nat had got over the initial shock.

With rugby mates, doing this over beer and a curry was the only way forward. Dan, however, didn't gauge his audience very well and began before everybody had arrived, meaning he ended up telling the tale three times over. It took less than five minutes before someone started taking the piss. Cheers, fellas!

Mates being mates, they responded in the only way they knew how. More beer and an in-depth discussion on the offending nut and its possible replacement.

There then followed a debate that would rival a UN convention on the probabilities of getting a really big replacement. Can you request a specific size and weight? Could you get an extra two – just how impressive would that be? Was it possible to acquire a titanium one? The grown-up, educated drinkers discussed all possible scenarios long into the night. Everyone was a dedicated expert. Dan found the evening both comforting and highly educational (well, not really the last bit).

The hangover the next day was so worth it. The world was back to relative normality, life carries on. When the pros and cons were discussed, Dan decided the prosthetic route was not for him: there would be no replacement.

IS NORMAL, NORMAL?

Dave was almost halfway through the first cycle of treatment after having a testicle removed, but was still feeling okay. And this puzzled him.

He checked with his medical team, and they were delighted with his progress. In the end, Dave began to realise that the best way for him to cope with his position was to almost expect to feel unwell, expect to wake up feeling the dreaded possible side effects of chemo that he had heard and researched about (Google is not always a good thing to have instant access to).

If he took this approach, whenever he woke up and felt fine he was euphoric, feeling a new zest for life, a freedom, sound in the knowledge that he was blessed. This really helped him through his days.

He knew it might not last forever, but was grateful for every minute he remained feeling 'normal'; it could, after all, change at any moment.

Until that happened, Dave made the very most of his wellbeing. Lunch with his wife, a few cheeky (off-cycle) beer days with mates, enjoying his rugby (watching, not playing, those days would come in the future), reappreciating all the good things in life.

Having always been a great lover of life, this new dimension just enhanced his appreciation all the more, especially if he could enjoy those days with family and friends.

WHEREVER YOU BE LET THE WIND BLOW FREE

It is fair to say that the list of possible side effects from the treatments involved in dealing with all forms of cancers goes on and on. It is, however, very much a game of Russian Roulette as to who gets what, if any.

Some effects can be debilitating, but there is one that can only really be viewed with humour. The sort of schoolyard humour of old that makes you belly laugh, which, by the way, makes it all the worse.

This side effect is chronic flatulence. It is not, by any means, the sneaky little squeaky fart that you can hide with a cough, door slam or clap. It has, in fact, been described as the mother of all noises.

In Peter's case it got to the point where every step he took was accompanied by the loudest trumpet. Birds flew from their perches in trees, outside, dogs ran to hide under the beds, neighbours two doors away were able to hear the crystal-clear parping. Peter could not help but laugh and laugh. This resulted in a fanfare that went something along the lines of laugh.. fart… laugh… fart louder… laugh… fart loudest!

Peter began to fear he may just blow away with the expelled gases and held on to every chair back, door handle and table top as he walked around the house. But one thing was for sure, there was absolutely no way he was going outside. No, this was a little something that had to be endured within the privacy of one's own home. There was the elderly, the very young and the infirm members of the public to consider, after all.

The tuneful day finally came to an end. Peter had laughed almost until he cried and as he drifted off to sleep he wondered whether he could have actually created a tune. Maybe tomorrow, a little experiment… should the situation remain.

IRRIGATION...
IRRIGATION...
IRRIGATION...
THAT'S WHAT
YOU NEED

Warning: Poo Content

Pat had been considering the 'irrigation' process for quite a while, conducting a great deal of research and spending a lot of time looking into the procedure and its possible benefits.

Although Cecil the stoma was generally behaving well, Pat was always on the lookout for any way to make both their lives easier. The less Cecil had to work the less Pat had to concern himself with him. No offence, Cecil.

The decision was made: Cecil and Pat were going to take their relationship to the next level.

The Irrigation Team were called in.

Okay, now imagine trying to poo with an audience. Yep, even with the team's professional guidance and input, it was a little surreal and an unusual experience, to say the least. No standing ovations or scorecards though.

So, here is how it works. Don your lab coat, safety goggles on and pens at the ready. Using a cone that fits into the stoma (stoma nurses demonstrated how to do this), makes for an interesting afternoon with, believe it or not, much laughter.

After feeding in about 1.5 litres of tepid water, the pressure around the stoma is such that the cone can be removed. A long plastic sleeve, which becomes a sort of tube, goes over the stoma and into the toilet bowl. Once the process got going, things were moving along and it was clearly going well.

There were plenty of gasps and 'That's the best one we've done yet', which was all very encouraging. Pat felt the day was considered momentous and could easily imagine it worthy of a mention around the nurses' dinner table that evening.

The process can take about forty minutes to one hour, but it means that afterwards a stoma cap can be worn rather than a bag. This allows for more fitted clothing, with no need for larger tee shirts. It also means a 'once a day' visit to the toilet and less likelihood of 'incidents'. Almost a 'normal' bum again.

Some find irrigation is only a once every other day occurance, or even up to three days (although that's possibly considered a little Russian Roulette on the stoma front).

Although irrigation isn't for everyone, it does work for many. All anyone wants is to make life a little easier for themselves.

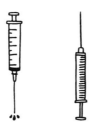

NO FOOLS AND XBOX RULES DAY

April 1st.

With a chemotherapy schedule agreed and the treatment plan moving forward and everything clear in his and his wife's minds, Dan now wanted to tell his boys about his illness and forthcoming treatments.

Lewis, being the eldest, of an age and having the level of intelligence to understand, got full chapter and verse. His first question to his dad was "When does it start?" Dan explained the dates and timescales, explaining furthermore his need to get all the information together before telling his son. Dan also made his eldest offspring promise that if he had ANY questions, to ask him or his mum and not to

Google anything. Google can be the enemy in some situations, and this definitely was considered one of them. Lewis agreed.

Telling Ollie, the youngest, was going to be a very different conversation.

Dan explained carefully that he needed some medicine to get rid of some bad cells, and if he had any worries about anything to ask his parents.

"Now, this medicine might make me tired and feel poorly and make my hair fall out." Ollie's response was classic: "Well, that's just stupid – having a medicine that makes you poorly. Can I go on the Xbox now?"

Dan had to smile, there was one happy and so far completely unfazed fella.

Dan felt happier knowing his boys now knew about his illness and what the immediate future might hold. It meant that things could be talked about – perhaps not completely openly, but he didn't have to try to hide what was going on. They were a family, Team Cook, and they were in this together.

The best news to both boys was that yes, the family was still going on holiday to Cornwall the following week. A place where Dan and his family knew they could completely relax and disconnect for a while.

θ θ θ θ θ θ θ θ

ROID RAGE

It was only when Roger had allowed himself ten minutes to read the warning leaflet that came with his steroids did he find it a real page turner.

By all accounts he could have all or any of almost fifty different side effects. The steroid was given to help his body repair itself, particularly after chemotherapy. He had been taking it for almost five weeks now. When he thought of it like that he realised he had, so far, been lucky, having had none of the nasty side effects. Yes, it was fair to say Roger was feeling a little smug with his findings.

The Commonwealth Games was on the television and as he wasn't working he decided he would spend the afternoon watching the day's events. Just as he was settling down into his comfortable chair, his wife brought him a cup of tea.

"Thought I'd watch some of the Games," he said, taking the cup from her.

"There's the netball finals on next," she smiled.

Deciding he had nothing to lose, Roger got comfy. It was England versus Australia. Now Roger wasn't a true follower of the sport, it had to be said, and yet he couldn't help but get caught up in the fast-paced, dramatic match. He had been warned that the steroids prescribed to aid his recovery could make him a little moody, irritable even, and possibly a little bombastic on occasion.

His wife, however, had been completely honest with him and told him she had seen absolutely no change. Until that is, the netball match. By the middle of it Roger was almost standing on his chair screaming for England to win. Both teams were playing out of their skins. The countdown clock was ticking, and Roger was by now jumping up and down, the air blue. His wife was a little shocked, she had no idea Roger even knew those words, so she steered well clear of the lounge. With the last second to go, England scored a final point. The game ended 52 – 51, England won Gold.

By this time Roger was hoarse. His wife stood in the doorway, wearing a look of both shock and relief – the game had ended.

Roger climbed down from his standing position on the armchair, smiled as he walked past his wife. "Time for a beer I think," he called as he passed her.

"Mmmm… think perhaps those steroids may be taking effect after all," she called after him. She quickly turned off the television and followed her husband into the kitchen. The victory for England was history-making, 2018 would definitely be a year to remember. Roger's wife thought about this as she straightened the furniture. As she passed through the room, she admitted to herself that she was just pleased that only the chair, nor anything else, had been broken.

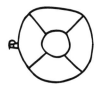

ENTER RONNIE

Pat had begun his treatment. His surgery, to give him what was commonly referred to as 'Barbie Bum', courtesy of being diagnosed with rectal cancer, had been completed.

His rehabilitation with the help of his wife, best friend and soulmate Paula was ticking along nicely. There were of course the odd bumps in the recovery road, but Paula and Pat navigated their way around them as best they could. They were both making adjustments to carry on as best they could with normal life, but were determined not to allow their lives to be defined by cancer, the treatments or any other aspect of their current situation. They were both of the opinion that 'life is life', and not matter what it threw at you, the alternative of no life at all was far worse.

Pat and Paula had always loved eating out; they had favourite restaurants, and hotels they loved to stay at, but also loved exploring and trying out new places and cuisines.

Having had the surgery on what was already a painful bum – a true 'pain in the arse' (pun absolutely intended) – Pat had purchased a comfort ring, the sort of device used by anyone from pregnant women to haemorrhoid sufferers. It was a state-of-the-art, memory foam jobbie that had been recommended for his recovery from surgery.. A real Rolls-Royce of derriere indulgence.

At first Pat had said he would never be taking 'Ronnie' – the name given to the ring by Paula, now held with a modicum of affection after they had grown close – out in public, but as time went on and he and Paula settled into their new life, it seemed less and less of an issue. A date was chosen, they were going to enjoy a lunch out. Ronnie was coming too.

Pat, even prior to his diagnosis, had been very much a 'get on with it' kind of guy. This attitude didn't change when he was told he had cancer. There was a quote from Charles R. Swindoll that he liked to live by: "Life is ten percent what happens to you and ninety percent how you react to it."

Ronnie had a bag of his own, which looked like any other you might take shopping. The restaurant Pat and Paula chose was perfect and their lunch date long awaited. Thinking ahead, they had already discussed how they would co-ordinate the delicate ring manoeuvre so as not to draw attention. Being keen ballroom and Latin dancers, they possessed the skills to easily execute this minor 'quick step'.

As they were shown to their table they were delighted with their choice – so far, so good. When Paula took her seat discreetly she slipped the bag under the table, and, in one effortlessly fluid movement the ring was on Pat's chair and he was sitting comfortably. In fact, he delighted in feeling a little smug when he realised that without the ring his seating position would not have been great for him anyway. And so a lovely lunch was enjoyed, Ronnie unseen yet offering the greatest of comfort. *Strictly Come Dancing* had nothing on these two.

SAVING THOSE SWIMMERS

Dan and Nat had NO plans to have any more children, their adored two sons Lewis and Ollie being more than capable of keeping them constantly on their toes. It had been recommended to Dan that saving some sperm was a sensible idea, as chemotherapy had the nasty habit of making people sterile. There could, in the future, be the question "Why didn't you do it?" if he had chosen not to take the advice.

Once agreed, Dan was referred to the andrology department at Hammersmith Hospital. Having never made a sperm deposit before, this was a tad nerve-racking and most definitely uncharted territory. After dropping youngest son Ollie off at school, Dan and Nat made their way to the hospital. Dan did wonder whether her accompanying him was more for the amusement factor than perhaps a purely supportive role – the look of sheer horror on the face of every bloke in the waiting room when they sat down was a sight. Was that a smile he saw pass over her lips?

Having filled out a ton of paperwork, Dan was present with 'the cup'. The extremely efficient-looking nurse announced "Room one, Mr. Cook," closely followed by, "There are magazines in the drawer, or a DVD if you wish." This information was delivered in the same manner as an assistant at Tesco might direct you to the flour in the baking section. Avoiding eye contact with anyone, Dan made his way to the room.

He had absolutely no intentions of touching anything in that room. It was one of those situations where this was definitely one of the last places he wanted to be, but he knew it needed to be done.

Magazine? No thank you, he wasn't going anywhere near that drawer, let alone its contents. He dreaded to think who had been at either.

DVD? That would mean touching a remote control. Ugh! No, that wasn't happening either.

Good old imagination was the order of the day – it never fails. Deposit made, job done. Dan's mind screamed, "Get me out of here," closely followed by his body and his wife. That was part one of the job done anyway. Yes, to add a little insult to injury they like you to repeat the procedure. Two deposits, please.

That is for another day.

OLYMPIC HOPES

Mike had managed to keep his diagnosis quiet from his work colleagues for some time. He felt well enough to work and had somehow managed to navigate his life around appointments, treatments and symptoms. As his appearance wasn't affected too much, cancer often being a 'silent' illness, he carried on with life as normally as possible, feeling this was the approach that worked best for him in dealing with his cancer.

It was only when he started taking steroids as part of his treatment that his appearance changed dramatically. When his face began to swell, and he got the full measure of the 'moon face' side effects, he knew he could not keep his illness to himself any longer.

Being a sales executive for an office furniture company, and constantly meeting clients and suppliers face-to-face, he was slightly concerned for his work.

In fact he had no cause to be worried, and when the news was revealed there was nothing but full support from everyone, from the managing director down.

The head office for his employer was very near the Russian Embassy in London. There was a conference to be attended by all sales staff, and Mike was looking forward to getting together and catching up with everyone he didn't often get to see in person. It was a great team-building event too, and forged relationships no end.

He knew there would be questions asked, but he was prepared and looking forward to the 'after conference' fun of socialising with some great friends and colleagues.

The conference was a busy affair, with lots of speakers, target projections and new product lines showcased. Mike sat with the other regional sales executives and happily joked about the steroid treatment and how he could outperform any athlete in strength and speed, laughing that at that moment in time he would fail a drug test spectacularly.

At lunch time a large group of the sales staff ventured out to take in a little of what central London had to offer. As the group passed the Russian Embassy, one of Mike's colleagues shouted across the group, "Mike, quick, get yourself in there; you'll be signed up in a heartbeat for the next Olympics. You'll be a sensation, no questions asked." The group fell about laughing. Mike agreed, "Ah, yes, my Olympic dreams would come true after all."

The group proceeded to take bets on Mike's chances in each organised event. It was agreed that with his steroid intake he could beat all comers, including the entire Russian team. Mike was an athletic superstar without even stepping foot on a track. An enthusiastic and highly amusing lunch was taken by the group.

PUMPS, RINGS AND ALL MANNER OF THINGS

Sam never thought he would ever be thinking about erectile dysfunction, let alone experiencing it. Initially he was almost in denial. This wasn't like a 'blip' caused by over indulgence on the beer front or not being 'in the mood'. This was dysfunction on another level, a completely flacid fella. What man wants to acknowledge that, ever?

It was only when he met other men in the same position at a support session at Maggie's (cancer support centre) that he allowed himself to acknowledge the problem. It is said that recognising there is a problem is half the way to solving it. Well, this sentiment was perhaps slightly ambitious, but he felt he was certainly ready to deal with the matter.

There was a lot of humour in the group. It was then that Sam began to realise that this was so often the case when men got together – they make fun of a serious subject, and end up even poking fun at themselves. This was how men dealt with so many problems. Once all the barriers were down it was so much easier. Before long, talk of lubricants, rings to help with maintaining an erection and a whole bunch of other aids that could be tried was free flowing. Sam laughed with the rest of the group.

The huge weight he had been carrying around after his run-in with cancer had been lifted. Armed with newly acquired information, some aids, even a few top tips you were not going to find in any medical leaflet, he felt happier than he had in what seemed like an age. Sex was for having fun, it had just lost the fun part when there was a bump in the road. Sam knew he had to approach getting things back on track with fun too, learn to find the playful part of 'getting back in the saddle' He was sure the rest would follow.

Sam knew his partner had already shown she was happy to wait, be patient and that he needed to come to terms with things in his own way. Well, he was in a good place now and there was a sense to make the effort on his part.

He passed a florists and bought a dozen red roses, then a bottle of champagne. And with his bag of 'goodies' and information that he had acquired, he was going to put phase one of his newly formed plan into action. The main aim was to remind the love of his life that this was still very much what she was. The rest would take time and patience, but it would all be dealt with as something to enjoy, and he was sure together they would do just that.

Instead of feeling like he was in some way failing, he now felt like he was almost being naughty, even laughing to himself at what he had planned. He marvelled at how a situation, if thought of in a completely different manner, can suddenly work for you. His 'bag of tricks' felt more like 'toys' now, and that in itself made him feel all the more 'up for it'.

Sam had learnt of other methods like pumps that could be fitted if his 'toys' didn't work, but for now he was happy to take the first baby steps and have fun trying them out. Having fun trying things out together was the important first step.

TAKE A SEAT
(WOULD IF I COULD)

When every part of your body, after being provided with a 'barbie bum', and everybody around you (including your consultant), says you can't sit still for too long, you have to listen.

There remains, however, the fact that you have to attend appointments. Being unable to drive is one thing, but not being able to actually sit in a car is a major hurdle too.

Pat found himself in this predicament. He needed to attend various appointments but knew he was in no fit state to sit through the journey. Rectal surgery will do that to you. It remains a pain in the arse for quite some time (excuse the pun).

Paula was more than happy to drive her husband wherever he needed to be, but it still didn't solve the actual problem of how he was going to get to those places, literally.

Pat then came up with an idea: he would have to lie across the back seat of Paula's car.. Then when they arrived at their destination he would have to effectively 'back out' of the car. It would be an understatement to say Pat and Paula laughed out loud at what they must have looked like on the various CCTVs that hospitals and medical centres delighted in having in vast numbers in their grounds and car parks.

They could imagine the scene:

So, woman pulls up in car. Checks her mirrors, taking note of who is around, the fewer spectators the better. The coast is clear. Trying not to look furtive she then gets out and opens the rear driver's-side door. Very slowly, ever so carefully, a man extricates himself from the back seat, feet, legs and bottom first until he is standing.

Pat and Paula often wondered what those monitoring the cameras must have thought of the sight.

Was this a form of punishment for the husband? Perhaps a little something they liked to do for kicks? Had the husband lost a bet and this was the forfeit or, heaven forbid, had he left the toilet seat up one too many times? Alternatively, had she kidnapped him? Although, kidnapping someone per se was not entirely improbable, but then taking them to a local hospital...? Not so much.

The list went on and on and provided countless amusing moments.

"CASHIER NUMBER TWO PLEASE." ACTUALLY, DEPOSIT NUMBER TWO

With the holiday date looming ever closer, Dan was aware he had a limited timetable to get his second sperm deposit done at Hammersmith.

He was up first thing and at the andrology department when it opened. Hardly a January sale type of affair, but he needed to be one of the first in. More paperwork, several blokes sitting around looking decidedly uncomfortable, zero eye contact. This was definitely not a meet-up at the local boozer kind of place, no light-hearted banter or discussing the football or rugby scores. Nat didn't accompany him on this occasion; Dan mused that the other occupants had no idea what they were spared.

Room number two this time. Maybe these places could do with the same announcer as used in banks and post offices: "Cashier number two, please". Same drill as before. Dan avoided the drawer with the 'magazines' and the option of the DVD. Imagination ruled, job done, once again Dan signed the paperwork and was out the door in record time.

He was told he would have to go back at some point for a consultation, but until that consultation happened nobody was allowed to use the sperm, including Dan!

That consultation could wait for another day, Dan decided, as he headed off for further tests to clear the way for the much anticipated family holiday, where talk of treatments, side effects and everything other than enjoying family life, creating memories and great times could be forgotten.

DIFFUSE LARGE B CELL NON-HODGKIN'S LYMPHOMA

That title is quite a mouthful, as was the number of pills Peter was now taking to combat his run-in with this type of cancer.

Being a man with what could be considered a slightly warped sense of humour, he took the new additions to his daily routine in his stride. The treatment plan he was placed on meant he had two doses of chemotherapy via I.V., the 'Gin and Tonic' sessions, as he liked to call them, followed by a smorgasbord of multi-coloured pills taken on a daily basis – these, he was convinced, made him sound like a rattlesnake, and he joked that he was afraid to fart in case he blew the seat off his jeans and peppered the cats with psychedelic NHS buckshot.

Along with a good dose of prednisolone for added umph, he felt there was a very real danger of casualties of both animal and human variety should he get close and let one rip.

Living on the edge of farmland, Peter thought a walk in the back garden, keeping an eye out for local wildlife of course, was perhaps the safest option. He checked first for any neighbours who might have had similar intentions – going out into the garden, that is, not preparing to break wind.

He had no intention of appearing on the news under the headline: "Local man arrested for causing assault with deadly fart."

What Peter wasn't expecting was that the chemo via I.V. would make him feel pretty trippy, and it has to be said he did comment that he felt a little 'on cloud nine' at times. His wife likened his behaviour to having a nine-year-old hyperactive boy in the house again. Amusing for an hour or two; utter exhaustion setting in after any longer.

As with any 'up' there must be a 'down'. This

followed a day or two later when the nine-year-old boy became the sullen 'emo' teenager.

Peter and his wife being in their retirement years made for an interesting time, certainly never dull. Yes, Peter, Sue, their cats and dogs had to learn to adjust to their new life, but this they did with a certain degree of laughter and humour.

NOT EXACTLY NICKY CLARKE

Myer had been an oncology nurse for ten years. During this time she had been involved with and nursed people through all aspects of cancer and oncology treatments.

There was only one thing, one simple aspect, which she dreaded more than anything: helping people shave their heads. Although she dreaded it, she never refused, and sometimes it was even where the most fun was to be had.

One particular occasion, when she was called upon for her most feared task, was with a young man of about twenty who had suffered hair loss as soon as he started his chemotherapy treatment. He was studying to be a dentist, 6' 2" and weighed 100 kilos – not a small man by any means.

This young man's hair was a mass of thick curls and he needed it all gone. But before it was removed he wanted to have some fun. Myer, as always, was a tad nervous. The young man asked if she could shave it first of all into a Mohawk style. Myer promised she would do her best but couldn't guarantee the results. The patient took pictures on his mobile phone throughout the process, with he and Myer laughing at all the weird stages his hair went through as it was being removed.

Myer was the first to admit she was no Nicky Clarke, but between them and the fits of laughter, the result was pretty impressive.

The young man sent pictures to his mates, and then in a flash he sent one last picture to his mother. With that done, the none-too-small and somewhat imposing man quickly asked for the Mohawk to be shaved off completely, before his mum arrived and truly told him off. His friends were very impressed with his somewhat short-lived hairstyle. His mother… not so much.

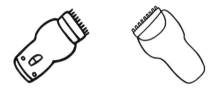

BACK TO BLACK

When Dan realised his hair was falling out he knew he had to take measures. Going along to his barbers he explained his predicament.

In no time the clippers were out and expertly wielded – that was it, Dan was hair-free! It certainly didn't look like him staring back in the mirror. He knew instantly he would never really like it, him being bald just didn't sit right in his mind, but it did make the whole anxiety of hair loss a bit less intimidating. There were, after all, countless men sporting buzzcuts by choice.

Dan also knew that after his treatment and his hair had grown back he would not be one of those. Although many people commented on how much the hair-free look suited him, it wasn't him. Mind you, the barber not charging for the cut was a nice way of softening the blow.

Dan's mates, in true mate fashion, more than made up for that by continuing to take the piss, along with taking bets as to whether his hair would grow back curly, straight, or even... ginger! Suffice to say they were disappointed when in fact it did not. Though it did grow back in his normal shade (but with a little more grey than he remembered, that absolutely must have been a chemo effect...), it was so baby soft, so touchably, run your fingers through it soft, that he was convinced he could have done a Johnson's Baby Shampoo advert... nice!

YOU'LL NEVER WALK ALONE

Mike was a member of Cambridge United's supporters club. He would stand and watch with the same group of friends every Saturday, he loved the camaraderie as much as the football. When he finally decided to tell his group of mates one Saturday afternoon that he had prostaate cancer, the group fell silent.

It was obvious nobody knew what to say, until one of them finally spoke up. "It is the most common cancer for men. Many have different treatments and outcomes differ." He ended with, "I'm sure you'll be alright, Mike." Mike was thankful for the statement as, he suspected, were the rest of the group. The heavy silence was broken. It was appreciated by all.

Mike had his surgery.

Cambridge United were playing at home. It was the first game Mike had missed due to prostate cancer. At 3pm there came a text. It read: "At the slightest sign of cancer you are not here. What's the matter with you?" Mike would have laughed out loud if he wasn't still suffering from the after-effects of the operation. He certainly felt good at having received the text and mused how odd it was that someone berating you can have such a great effect and lift your spirits.

He replied with a text saying he was at home, nice and warm, being made lots of cups of tea, eating biscuits and listening to the commentary on the radio, in the hope of making them jealous. It didn't work.

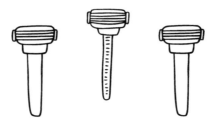

SHAVE?...
NOT SHAVE?

Hair loss. Not just top-of-the-head hair loss – all-over hair loss.

Now, for a man this often means goodbye razor, shaving and all the accoutrements and paraphernalia that go along with this. Depending on whether you are a man who has to shave once a day regardless, or every few days, there is a little novelty to realising you don't have to spend that time carrying out the tedious task.

If, however, you are a bearded man, the effect can be very disconcerting, even more shocking than losing the hair on your head. Thought-provoking stuff, discovering you may have an extra chin, or worse, chins that you have never had to encounter before.

As for silky-smooth legs? Not generally a priority for the male population, and a little startling when first noticed, but if you are a competitive bodybuilder, professional cyclist or just plain 'a little out there', this look may work for you. Just saying, is all.

What is undeniable is that these little day-to-day occurrences make you really appreciate things even more when they start returning to normal. The five o'clock shadow makes an appearance – cause for celebration, break out the champers! Or at least a brewski.

If you had a beard, it slowly but surely returns, and you will love it all the more. You will want to spend a little extra on that trim or try new hairstyles, guaranteed.

The household fight for the last razor will have more meaning and, though not always admitted to, appreciated tenfold.

QUESTIONING PROFESSOR HAWKING

Peter had been at sea from the age of fifteen; the ocean was his calling. After many decades of circumnavigating the globe, aboard everything from tankers to cruise liners, he and his family had settled in Essex – Mersea Island to be exact.

Peter had married a beautiful South African nurse and they had two children; they were all used to sunnier climes and Mersea came as a bit of a shock. Although originally from Plaistow, Peter had loved everything about South Africa. The family had moved back to England in 1986 when he had the job of outfitting a cruise ship called *The Astor* from top to bottom.

It was only when he was diagnosed with a very rare form of cancer and had to undergo a dramatic and life-changing operation – a radical amputation – that he slowed down. During his hospitalisation he had many visitors, one of his regulars being his nephew Del. Del was renowned for his mischievous antics, and had brought a smile more than once to his uncle's face throughout the cancer treatment and rehabilitation.

Peter was an avid reader, a highly intelligent man, and was working his way through two of Professor Stephen Hawking's books. On one occasion Del's visit coincided with a particularly down day for Peter; Del could see he was going to have to pull out all the stops to help his uncle. After he messed around with the copious amounts of rubber gloves that were to hand in Peter's room – to the exasperation of the nurses – Peter's mood had lifted a little.

When Peter was taken for therapy, Del found the two books on his uncle's bedside cabinet. Del knew Peter would be some time and had an idea for something to leave his uncle when he returned.

Del returned the following day; he could hear his uncle before even seeing him. Peter was sitting up in bed, voicing his outrage at what he was reading. Del was privileged enough to be greeted by a barrage of expletives, as Peter explained how ridiculous he found Hawking's writing and findings. He was in the middle of ranting about how the world-renowned theoretical physicist couldn't write a book for toffee, and how he continually contradicted himself, and was frankly a fool.

It was as Peter saw his nephew's reaction that he realised something was afoot. "Go on, what did you do?" Del reached into the bedside cabinet. Realisation spread across Peter's face. "You swapped the books around, didn't you?" There followed another tirade of unprintable words – the bookmark had been placed on the same page but in the second book.

As Del left Peter's bedside that day and made his way down the corridor, he was pleased with the fact that his uncle could still be heard laughing, albeit punctuated with the occasional curse.

MAN BABY

Looking back, there was a silver lining to all that had gone on. Nick was revelling in the new lease of life he had with his son, spending lots of time together doing silly things, like skipping through town. Nick couldn't have cared less, his sole focus was on his son and having fun with him. True, they did get some funny looks. Why was Gollum from *Lord Of The Rings* running through the town, skipping along with a child? As no police or social services were called, Nick guessed he couldn't have scared anyone too much.

Even when the chemotherapy made Nick very poorly, he never lost the ability to have fun. However, it had not been an easy journey.

At first the news had been devastating. The cloud of despair was all engulfing and the questions came thick and fast. When am I going to die, is it next week, next month, next year? What about my son? How do I tell him? These questions hit like a hammer blow.

Being a little nervous, Nick wanted to know when his chemotherapy was going to start. He thought he had the Christmas period to process the information he had been given, but there was to be another shock – he was to start his treatment six days later. Wow! The hits just kept on coming.

By December Nick was enjoying a cup of tea with his parents, having completed the first cycle of his chemotherapy. He absentmindedly stroked his beard, and a clump came off in his hand; and there was another shock when he checked his hair (he was normally bald but was currently sporting a sort of 'monk do') – yep, it had begun to fall out. Nick went home, took a razor to what was left and got rid of the lot.

After a day or so, Nick began to kinda like his new look; yes, he was rocking it. He may have likened his appearance to a fetus, a man baby, particularly when came the day he was completely hairless – yes, even down there. Strange feeling, strange look. It still made him smile when he recalled that the weirdest aspect of being completely 'body bald' was breaking wind for the very first time, fearing he had in fact experienced 'follow through', but hugely relieved to discover a fart was just a fart after all.

Not even when he resembled Fungus The Bogey Man after catching a cold, coupled with an infection towards the very end of his treatment and there being sufficient gunk emitted that the title seemed entirely apt, did he give up on what life had to offer. Nick was adamant his life was what he made of it, and he made so very much of every minute with his friends, family and fun. He also went on to marry again, inherit a second son and is loving life.

VINDALOO...DON'T MIND IF I DO.

Steve had endured his rounds of chemo with his usual bravado. He had experienced some of the warned-about side effects but still felt he had come away fairly unscathed.

He had found chewing gum helped with the almost permanent dry mouth. If he felt ulcers beginning to form he would try a milkshake, the alkaline of the milk helped a little with the discomfort. Also, an unusual but handy tip for itchy hands and feet (having begun to wonder if he was developing athlete's foot, the toes on one foot being so itchy) was to rub Vick's Vapour Rub on his feet and even his hands for some relief (hoorah! for the internet and people's crazy cures). All these things are worth remembering and trying, he decided.

114

Having had only occasional nausea, he found peppermint tea helped alleviate the symptoms a little. Mind you, he did wonder if it was more the disgusting taste of the tea that helped distract his mind from the feeling of nausea.

About six weeks after the end of his treatment had ended, Steve noticed some unusual changes in himself. He had always been a cider drinker, but now he preferred bitter, and he had always been someone who couldn't really handle spicy food. A chicken korma to him was as much of a spicy kick as he could endure. His preference with food had always been creamy sauces, mild cheeses and subtle flavours.

It was only when he was enjoying a night out with the lads, treatment over and feeling on top of the world, did Steve discover his tastes had changed, not just a little bit but dramatically. It was the first real night out he had had in an age. The treatment had taken a little over six months in total, and this, coupled with six weeks of recovery, meant it was a while before he felt he was himself again. The evening was planned by Steve's mates and had been in the diary for some time. He was not the 'designated driver', so Steve had decided he was going to enjoy it. When (after a few beers to start with) the waitress came to take the group's food order, they decided, among other dishes, they would partake in the 'Challenge Chicken Wings' – chicken wings in a buffalo sauce made with Scotch Bonnet chilli peppers.

It was to be a shared challenge, and the idea was that the first person to eat most of the wings, sauce and everything that came with the dish was to be the winner. The group, Steve included, were all laughing at his ability, or the lack of it, to eat spicy food, and it was generally agreed that he would come last. But it would be a laugh to see who exactly would win.

The bets were in and a little wager was placed by each man. The Challenge Wings arrived. It was agreed nobody would eat their main course until the challenge had been completed. The 'dumbing down' of taste buds was not allowed with either food or drink. The challenge was on.

First to go was Mick, the largest member of the group. In his own eyes, a world-renowned 'hot chilli' eater. The first molten mouthful went down easily. The same was said for each member of the rest of the group. Then it was Steve's turn. There was much heckling and jostling as he prepared to down the forkfull. The general consensus was this would be his first and last mouthful.

The forkful of fiery spice went down easily. No one was more surprised than Steve himself. There was the odd accusation that perhaps he had consumed contraband in the form of cough sweets or something similar to numb his mouth. Round two was the same. By round three some of the group had conceded defeat and by round four there were only three contestants left in the running, Steve being one of them.

Steve couldn't believe it, not only did he find the heat and spiciness of the dish palatable, but he was actually really enjoying every mouthful – another first. In the next round the other two challengers conceded, and just to prove he really was enjoying his newfound tastes, he finished off the dish completely.

"Next time fellas, whose up for a vindaloo?" Steve laughed.

Chemotherapy hadn't just made him well again it had resulted in a whole different and new side to himself. Steve was loving it, although he wasn't however sure how much his girlfriend would appreciate his breath later.

THESE BOOTS ARE MADE FOR WALKING

Barry was a keen walker. After his prostatectomy he had wanted to indulge his passion all the more. A lust for life after the drama of the diagnosis of prostate cancer, surgery and the subsequent after-effects made him appreciate even more what life has to offer. He felt privileged to have been given another chance, another bite at the cherry.

As time wore on and he was able to take up more walking trips and excursions, Barry began to feel that incontinence during long walks was becoming a real problem.

It was suggested that the use of an external catheter could be the way forward. In order to go ahead with this, Barry had to be 'fitted' for it. The fitting involved two nurses, measuring both length and girth of his penis. Interesting, to say the least. Then came the actual fitting, one of the nurses holding the penis while the other nurse rolled the condom-type device on. So that the device would stay in place, the penis had to be held for a while so that the gel on the inside of the 'condom' bonded with the penis.

It would be fair to say that there was a time where such a tableau could have been considered almost dream-like. There may also have been a time when Barry (in fact, probably almost any male on the planet for that matter) would be grateful to be so accosted by two females, nurses at that!

It was, however, a one time only affair, and after the fitting had been demonstrated and Barry was clear on the instructions for performing the task himself, it became time for removing the catheter, or 'Conveen'. This was not such a 'pleasurable' experience. In fact, it was excruciatingly painful. Consider, if you will, a plaster being ripped off your most sensitive region. In Barry's opinion however, what was worse was that he had an afternoon appointment – his bladder did not fare so well in the afternoon and so he was somewhat desperate for the toilet by the time the nurses had finished. Perhaps not his finest moment, he considered.

However, Barry found the gains from using the 'Conveen' or external catheter have allowed his life to continue with great walking adventures, and he is a firm supporter of the device. So, if like Barry you enjoy outdoor activities or just an active lifestyle, this may be the way forward for you.

DRIER IF I HAD BEEN IN A CAR WASH

Dan had never been a man to sport a buzzcut. Short back and sides? Definitely. A long, shaggy Bon Jovi look? Not that he would ever admit to or provide evidence of, no. However, what Dan was completely unaware of and has a new-found respect for is those of us who are cranially hair-free, by whatever means. And if it's through choice, you are a far braver person for sure.

Chemotherapy had seen to it that Dan's hair was going, and he had to do something about it. Being honest, it was more a case of realising that the little clumps that were being deposited on the pillow, closely followed by more in the shower, meant the decision to go the whole hog and be rid of what was left was made. No comb-over attempts to be made here.

Stepping out of the barbers he was overcome by two emotions. The first was self-consciousness on a grand scale. Was everyone looking at him now he was effectively bald? Obviously, no, no they were not. Nobody who walked past turned and stared, nor was he paid any further attention than he might have been on any other occasion. The second emotion was a degree of vulnerability; even short hair can be seen as something to hide behind, it is part of our persona. There is also the feeling of not being quite as protected from the elements as before.

Anyway, fighting these two emotions and putting his best efforts into giving off an air of confidence – yes, I chose to do this – he made his way down the busy street.

Having only gone a few shop fronts down, he felt the first 'plop'. The sky darkened quickly and within seconds there was a downpour. Dan had no idea of the consequences of torrential rain and a bonce that was now as smooth as a baby's bottom. There is zero absorption other than your clothes. Very quickly, Dan realised why a hat, be it a flat cap, baseball, beanie – it matters not – is often sported by those with no hair in inclement weather.

He did begin to wonder whether there had ever been a case of drowning by downpour. If not, he thought, I may well be the first. Dan actually felt as if he were standing in a carwash, hardly able to catch his breath. He had never been so soaked, so quickly. The water fell like a sheet over his face, straight down his neck and in his ears. Yes, ears can get waterlogged in rain. The collar of his coat did nothing other than fill like a sponge, and then, when it had reached capacity, water steadily seeped down his neck, chest and back.

The only thing that might have helped would have been a squeegee. Soaked to the bone, in a very literal sense, in a matter of minutes.

From that day Dan always kept a hat of some sort in his coats, his car, the wife's car and just about any place there was room to stuff one. After the first experience he did consider keeping a set of nose clips handy too.

UNCLE FESTER

Sid had felt lousy for a long time. Not only due to lethargy and a lack of appetite, but also from being unable to sleep at night, plus significant weight loss. All of this, accompanied by persistent nagging from his wife, finally saw him wind up at the doctors surgery.

That day he received the news he was dreading: he had non-Hodgkin's lymphoma. What followed next in the conversation was a complete blur and Sid was totally unable to recollect anything further.

Within two weeks he had a chemotherapy treatment plan in place. After scan upon scan he was told he had a very good chance of a complete recovery. Prednisolone was prescribed and his life took on a new dimension.

Sid marvelled at just how quickly he and his family adapted to the new way of life – driving to appointments, people organising their days around his needs. Sid felt truly blessed to have such amazing family and friends around him.

The effects from his treatment took hold quite quickly. He gained weight, lost all his hair, but his grandchildren took it all in their stride. In some respects more so than the adult members of the family.

It was almost winter time, Halloween was a couple of days away and the grandchildren were getting their costumes ready. Trick or treating was the order of the day, well, evening.

Sid had an idea. He found a huge woollen coat in a local charity shop. It was enormous, even for his now increased size. With dark circles courtesy of eyeshadow around his eyes, and his completely bald head, he made the perfect Uncle Fester from *The Addams Family*.

The grandchildren were delighted when Grandad joined them for the whole evening trick or treating. They beamed with pride when their friends said: "Your Grandad is so cool! His costume is ace." The trick-or-treat booty for that year was record breaking. Sid had a blast and was happy to share the treasure.

Watching his grandchildren chomping their way through the sweet treats, he had to smile at the irony that having cancer had given him the perfect Halloween costume and a permanent, unique memory of precious, fun times spent with his grandchildren.

As the saying goes, every cloud… has a silver lining.

EDITED NEWS

Peter was a man, much like any other man – he tended not to fuss. He was a person who was inclined to play things down and was in most cases a calm and measured individual.

This actually translates to: doesn't really say anything when something is wrong, until it is almost too late; puts off something as not being particularly important but actually is; a tendency to brush things aside.

These traits are borne out of protection and love for those closest to him, although some-times sprinkled with a large dose of denial.

When Peter discovered he had cancer he dealt with it in his usual manner. It was nothing really, everything will be fine. This was by no means a bad outlook, and better than being the other way for sure, but it can be a little confusing for loved ones, friends and family.

Peter's daughter was keen for updates on her father's treatment and how he was feeling/coping. She soon learnt that she had to adopt a two-pronged approach. She would message her dad directly and he would reply with plenty of upbeat, positive and often hilarious renditions of the day's activities, events and how he was feeling. This she would take huge comfort from as she knew that he was being 'Dad', which in itself was a great sign.

She would then message her step-mother and get the more realistic take on events.

If Peter was suffering a little from niggly aches and pains and wasn't quite as chipper as on previous occasions, she took this to mean that he was actually feeling pretty awful, wasn't getting out of bed until late, and was feeling down and a bit bad tempered. As he was perfectly entitled to feel. It was his language and she understood it completely.

This system allowed her dad to deal with his illness his way, protect his loved ones and keep things the way he wanted them – and his wife was able to provide a true account of her husband's state of health.

Dad did the edited version, step-mum did the warts-and-all.

The family was therefore both well informed and handling Peter's cancer 'their' way. There is only one rule when dealing with cancer: "There are no rules."

AHH, GOT A NEW FRIEND?

Day 1 Cycle 1

Dan arrived at Marsden Hospital in Sutton and was shown to Kennaway Ward. Blood tests, urine tests and having a canula installed was the order of the day.

Dan was given the daily menu to peruse, featuring breakfast, lunch and dinner with as much tea, coffee and biscuits on demand, much to wife Nat's amusement – she couldn't help but remark that the ward was more like a spa. All this as the day's sun shone through the large windows.

It was on the ward that Dan was introduced to Gethyn, a rugby lad (that is a guaranteed instant rapport) who played locally until he moved back to Wales. Gethyn had undergone the same surgery and was about to embark on the same BEP3 treatment with the same cycle dates. Firm 'chemo friends' status was established and posted, much to the amusement of Dan's 'Poppy Boys' (a group of friends who are the husbands of the mum's group at the local boys' school) and his rugby mates.

With this new 'friend' status being broadcasted, there then followed a deluge of 'friends' memes from *The Inbetweeners*. Gotta love your mates. Bastards.

CHEMO
CHROME DOME

Peter was on cycle two of his chemother-apy for his cancer treatment. He was feeling very lucky and his consultants and nurses were delighted with his progress.

He had, so far, experienced no nasty side effects, no nausea, nothing. That was until he noticed his eyebrows were thinning and his hair was beginning to, as he liked to put it, 'move away' from his head. This he truly felt was a small price to pay for getting well again. Having the sort of outlook and sense of humour he had, he mused at his reflection in the mirror as he contemplated his hair, or the continuing lack of it.

Yes, he felt he had invented a new hair-style, one he chose to call the 'Chemo Chrome Dome', an ultra-modern affair, suitable for all ages, though only the very daring may be so bold as to sport the style.

That said, it required very little styling, merely the arranging of just two hairs. This, he considered, was perfect for today's man on the go.

POOL TABLE, COLOURFUL DÉCOR, XBOX…

IS THIS THE HOSPITAL ARMS?

The last hurdle, the last bout of treatment, but there was no room at the inn!

Yes, the treatment was scheduled, but alas there was no bed on the usual ward. What to do? Nick was the youngest male on the ward he normally resided in, and fortunately there was an alternative. Seeing an opportunity for a little bartering, he asked if it was possible to have a room of his own. The nursing staff said they would see what they could do.

Not too long after he was asked to follow the nurse who was overseeing his treatment. Had he pushed his luck, was he about to be confined to a pipe-and-vent-filled basement, the clanging and hissing of the hospital bowels his only comfort and companion?

As they made their way through the corridors, it certainly didn't feel like he was heading to the murky depths of the building.

Nick was surprised – he did get his own room but it had four beds in it; but it mattered not, he was delighted. He did, however, note the colourful walls, a pool table and games console. The whole place looked more like a pub than a hospital ward.

Regardless, it was no problem, he was just pleased to be getting his treatment and in such amenable surroundings. It was in fact a children's ward. As it turned out this was no bad thing, in fact it was great! Playing pool and Xbox all day was most relaxing, and the kids were fantastic. Nick felt at home and loved the company of so many children; they were all so strong, going through the same thing as Nick, but never lost the ability to have fun and muck around. He truly felt it was a great way to finish his last round of treatment.

MAGGIE'S

Maggie's is a charity that offers free support to people with cancer and their family and friends through a network of Centres across the UK, online and abroad.

The original blueprint for the first Maggie's Centre was laid out by Maggie Keswick Jencks and her husband Charles Jencks during Maggie's treatment for secondary breast cancer at the Western General Hospital in Edinburgh. Maggie was determined that people should not lose the 'joy of living in the fear of dying' and believed that in order to live well with cancer people needed information and advice that would allow them to be a more informed participant in their own treatment. She discussed her ideas with her husband and her former oncology nurse Laura Lee, who is now Maggie's Chief Executive. They chose a small stable block in the grounds of the Western General to become the first Maggie's Centre. Maggie's Edinburgh opened in 1996 and Maggie's vision became a reality.

The support offered in each Centre is formed around an evidence based programme and includes practical advice on subjects such as nutrition, benefits and treatment options, group sessions including Men's, Women's and Young People's Groups, as well as sessions specific to cancer type. Professional staff including Cancer Support Specialists, Benefits Advisors and Psychologists are on hand to offer advice and Centre visitors can also find support from each other in any one of the communal areas including the famous Maggie's kitchen table. Other activities on offer at Maggie's Centres include yoga, tai chi, nutrition, creative writing, expressive art, relaxation and many more.

Built in the grounds of specialist NHS cancer hospitals, the Centres are warm and welcoming places, built to a specified design brief but all with their own individual character and style. To achieve this Centres are designed by world-renowned architects, designers and landscape gardeners such as Zaha Hadid, Richard Rogers, Norman Foster, Paul Smith and Dan Pearson, who give their time for little or nothing. Their skills deliver the calm, uplifting environments so important to the people who visit and work in Maggie's Centres.

For further information about Maggie's please go to:

www.maggiescentres.org

A LITTLE NOTE ON BATTLING FAT LADS

Team members Phil Russell, Mike Sullivan, James Breeze, Steve King, Simon Watts, Matt Grist, Dean Robinson, Sam Hill and Richard Ellis. Representing Battling Fat Lads in the FA People's Cup 2017 and 2018

Written by Phil Russell

The team was formed by a load of middle-aged and unfit people for a social event, with a pint in the local being a reward for the exercise!

Inevitably the league folded due to a lack of teams, which left us without any competitive football until we heard about the FA People's Cup.

Five-a-side football tradition dictates that you need a comedy name, so, in the pub, the name Battling Fat Lads was born (no explanation needed for the team name!).

In 2016, we entered the FA People's Cup. As there is no charge for the tournament we decided we would donate what we would normally pay for a five-a-side session to Sport Relief. We crashed out of the cup that year with stories to tell and a sense of achievement.

We started playing regularly, for fun, on a Monday night at Mirfield Sports Centre.

In 2017, we decided that by playing in the FA People's Cup we could use it as a platform to raise money for a charity. We chose the OddBalls Foundation because we were keen to do some promotion for men's health issues. We wore the best five-a-side shirts in football, thanks to OddBalls donation of the kit, and raised £540.

For 2018 we had bigger plans. We were back in the FA People's Cup and we even won our first game!!! We scored lots of goals but unfortunately it wasn't enough to stay in the tournament. It would not matter, we had raised £1,200 for OddBalls. Our beautiful eye-watering shirts started conversations on the touchline and enabled us to engage other players in health promotion discussions. This is what we all wanted and I was really encouraged by the conversations as I am a registered nurse.

We featured on the BBC Sport website, which resulted in plenty of attention from the football world, while promoting the OddBalls Foundation.

We have now been contacted by a group of cardiac rehabilitation patients from East London called Two Touch AFC, who asked us to help them raise money for their cardiac unit. We will once again wear our beautiful OddBalls strips, and we are lucky enough to proudly promote two worthy causes.

It will always be an honour to represent Odd-Balls and we'd love to carry on doing so for years to come.

P.S. A big thank you to my team mates Simon Watts, Mike Sullivan, Matt Grist, Dean Robinson, Sam Hill, James Breeze, Steve King and Richard Ellis for representing the Battling Fat Lads in the FA People's Cup 2017 and 2018.

GET YOUR BLOGGING ON!

Something that helped me massively when writing this book was the fact that some fellas had decided the way forward was to blog their journey with their cancer.

Each person had their own reason for blogging, providing a 'warts-and-all' account of every stage. It serves as a reminder to them, how far they have come and how they felt at the time, but it also provides 'real' information, removes taboos and raises awareness.

Here are some blogs that I have referenced.
Read them, they are just brilliant.

http://rugbysavedmylife.blogspot.co.uk
by Dan Cook

http://http279.wordpress.com
by Patrick Reeve

A SELECTION OF RECIPES FROM

RYAN RILEY
FOUNDER OF LIFE KITCHEN

CARBONARA WITH MINT AND PEAS

Serves 2-4

- 1 large onion

- 2 large garlic cloves

- 1 red or green chilli

- 200g smoked high-welfare lardons

- 100g parmesan, grated

- 4 eggs

- 500g tagliatelle or penne

- 1 large handful frozen peas

- Small bunch of mint, torn

Pulse the onion, garlic and chilli together in a food processor until finely chopped and place them in a frying pan with a tightly fitting lid. Add the lardons and a good pinch of salt. Sweat on a low heat for 20-30 minutes, stirring occasionally, until the onions have completely melted.

While the onions are cooking, beat the grated parmesan and eggs together in a medium-sized bowl and season well with salt and pepper.

Cook the pasta according to packet instructions in plenty of well-salted water. Two minutes before the end of the cooking time, take a ladle of the starchy pasta cooking water and add this to the parmsesan and egg mixture.

Now add the peas to the pasta water for the final minute. When the pasta is cooked, drain thoroughly and add it back into the pan. Working quickly tip the parmesan and egg mixture over the pasta and keep stirring and tossing, the sauce will take a minute or so to emulsify. Do not overheat or the eggs will scramble.

Tear the mint, scatter generously and serve.

CARAMELISED MUSHROOMS WITH HERBS AND LENTILS

Serves 2-3

- 15g dried porcini mushrooms

- 1 large onion

- 3 large garlic cloves

- 500ml chicken or vegetable stock

- 300g beluga lentils

- 1 bay leaf

- 100g shitake and button mushrooms, chopped

- 30g butter

- 2 lemons, zested and juiced

- 1 bunch of parsley, finely chopped

- 1 bunch of chives

Soak the porchini mushrooms in 500ml of boiling water for 20 minutes. Cut the onion in half and and lightly smash the garlic cloves.

Drain the porcini mushrooms, reserving the liquid apart from the last 50ml or so, as this tends to be a little gritty. Rinse the lentils under cold running water then tip into to a large saucepan. Add the mushroom liquid, 400ml of the stock, the onion, crushed garlic cloves, bay leaf and a little salt and pepper. Bring to the boil and simmer for 25 minutes.

Meanwhile melt 20g of the butter in a frying pan, add the button, shitaki and porcini mushrooms and cook over a medium-high heat until heavily caramlised, about 10-15 minutes.

Add the juice and zest of one lemon and half the parsley to the mushrooms and set aside.

Drain the lentils, discarding the garlic cloves and onion. Add the remaining butter, chives and parsely to the lentils and stir, taste and adjust the seasoning if nessecary.

For the gremolata, finely chop the remaining parsely, zest a lemon and grate in a garlic clove, mix together.

Spoon the lentils onto a plate, pile the mushrooms on top, squeeze the lemon juice over everything, top with the gremolata and serve.

SWEET GARAM MASALA AND VANILLA SPICED APPLE CRUMBLE
Serves 2-3

For the filling:

- 400g cooking apples
- 2 tbsp of sweet garam masala
- 1 tsp caster sugar
- 1 tsp vanilla paste
- A squeeze of lemon juice

For the topping:

- 100g flour
- 100 cold unsalted butter
- 50g, rolled oats/ Granola
- 1 tbsp vanilla paste

Pre heat the oven to 190oc.

Peel and core the apples, put them into a
medium saucepan with the garam masala,
sugar, vanilla, lemon and 1 tbsp water for 5
minutes until just soft.

In a processor, tip in the flour, vanilla
and cold butter and pulse until you have
even breadcrumbs. Mix the oats through
the mixture.

In a shallow dish, spread out the mixture
evenly and top with the breadcrumbs. Bake
for 20 minutes or until golden brown. Serve
with cream or custard.

HARISSA SALMON WITH FENNEL YOGHURT SALAD

- 2 wild salmon fillets

- 2 tbsp harissa paste

- 1 tbsp olive oil

- 1 fennel bulb, cut into matchsticks

- 3 tbsp yoghurt

- 1 lime, juice and zest

- 1 tsp Nigella seeds

- 1 lemon

Mix together the harissa and oil and coat the salmon fillets generously. Place into a 180oc oven for 8 minutes. Remove from the oven and set aside.

Cut the fennel into thin matchsticks, add to a bowl with the yoghurt, lime zest and lime juice, toss together.

Sprinkle over the nigella seeds and serve with a wedge of lemon. Season to taste.

HARISSA CAULIFLOWER LEAVES

- 2 tbsp harissa paste

- 1 tbsp olive oil

- Sea salt

- Cauliflower leaves

Mix together the harissa, oil and salt and brush over the cauliflower leaves. Roast at 180c for 20 minutes until the outer leaves are crispy and delicious!

PINEAPPLE TACOS WITH PRAWNS, CHILLI AND LIME

- 1 pineapple, peeled and sliced into thin rings

- 100g cooked cold water prawns

- 1 chilli, diced

- 2 limes, zest and juice

- 1 spring onion, shredded

- a handful of corriander

Peel the pineapple and slice thinly into rounds.

In a bowl, mix the cooked prawns with the chilli, lime zest and juice of one lime.

Toss through the spring onion. Fold the pineapple round in half to form a 'taco' shell fill with the prawn mixture, add the corriander and finish with a final spritz of lime. Enjoy!

Tip: For extra smokiness, char the pineapple round lightly on the BBQ.